THINKING SKILLS

Ages 10-12

Activities and ideas to develop thinking skills
across the National Curriculum

Sharon Shapiro

Advisor: Trevor Davies

A & C Black • London

CONTENTS

INTRODUCTION

Today's pupils are the problem solvers of the future. If children are taught factual knowledge only, they tend to respond with conventionally 'correct' answers rather than by exploring creative solutions. All pupils can learn to think critically and creatively. This book provides teachers with ideas and activities to help pupils develop these skills. The activities make an ideal complement to classroom work across the curriculum. They can be used in isolation, in sequence, or dipped into, as teachers require.

ABOUT THIS BOOK

TEACHERS' FILE

The teachers' file offers advice on how to make make the most of this book. It explains the different types of thinking strategies and how children can benefit from using them. There are ideas for classroom organisation, ICT tips, assessment ideas and suggestions for parental involvement.

QUICK STARTS

This section offers activity and game ideas that help to promote children's thinking skills. These activities require little or no preparation and can be used across various learning areas to complement existing lesson plans.

ACTIVITY BANK

The activity bank contains 29 photocopiable activities that cover thinking skills related to fluency and flexibility, questioning, originality, forced relationships, imaginative visualisation, creative thinking, critical thinking, categorising, interpreting and inferring and evaluation. The activities can be used in any order and are suitable for children working individually or in groups.

Photocopiable activities

CHALLENGES

These photocopiable task cards offer creative investigational challenges. They can be given to individual pupils or groups, and they can be used at any time and in any order. The task cards involve pupils in following instructions and completing tasks independently.

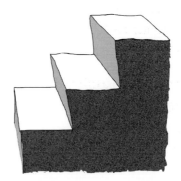

HOW TO USE THIS BOOK

QUICK STARTS

Quick starts are ideal warm-up activities for the beginning of a lesson. The activities are designed to be used flexibly: they can be used in any order and at any time. Each activity is intended to provide 10–15 minutes of group or whole class discussion.

Example

Which article? (page 14) provides an excellent opportunity to discuss media bias. The activity lends itself to initial group debate followed by a whole class discussion. Pupils could analyse a range of articles in local and national newspapers for bias.

Which article?

Select two newspaper articles giving accounts of the same event. Group pupils and have them study the articles, then discuss how the events are interpreted in each article. Are the events treated in a similar manner? If not, why do they think this might be so?

ACTIVITY BANK

These photocopiable activities can be used by individuals, groups or the whole class (with each child or pair of children referring to a copy of the sheet). An activity could provide the focus for a whole lesson (most of the activities require 30–40 minutes' investigation).

Example

Listing change (page 20) could be completed by groups or pairs of children. The activity asks pupils to consider rapid and slow change through science and geography contexts.

CHALLENGES

These activities are perfect for use in learning centres, in the school library or in the classroom. The investigational nature of the activities is in line with National Curriculum requirements such as AT1 in Maths and Science, and supports the development of investigational problem-solving skills.

Example

An unusual animal (page 46) offers children the opportunity to be imaginative about the appearance and habits of their made-up animal. Encourage children to apply their knowledge of science and the natural environment as they carry out the activity.

TEACHERS' FILE

What are thinking skills?

As well as helping children to think clearly, thinking skills enable them to collect information critically and creatively and to use this information to solve problems. Pupils also become more aware of decision-making processes as they develop their thinking skills. Through the activities in this book, children will learn thinking skills that encourage them to look at a variety of ideas, investigate in greater depth, practise more critical decision-making, challenge accepted ideas, approach tasks in decisive ways and search for misunderstandings, while keeping the aims of the task clearly in mind. As a result, their decisions will be more reliable, they will have a deeper understanding of concepts, their ideas will be more creative, they will examine content more critically and their work will be more carefully crafted.

Why do children need to develop thinking skills?

Children need to be able to judge, analyse and think critically in order to participate fully in a democratic and technological society. This can be achieved if the school as a whole recognises the value of thinking skills and provides opportunities for the thinking processes to be modelled and developed. All pupils can improve their thinking abilities, regardless of age, race, socio-economic status or different learning modes.

The basic skills are generally regarded as literacy and numeracy. These involve processes such as computation, recall of facts and the basic mechanics of writing. Once these fundamental skills have been mastered, children need to move on to more challenging tasks that will help them to understand more complex ideas. It is not necessarily true that pupils who can find the correct answers to problems have learnt thinking skills. Pupils need plenty of practice before they can tackle problems that require them to use advanced thinking skills. The cognitive operations that make up thinking need to be explored, explained, taught and practised many times before they can be mastered.

Some basic tips

Allow students to be nonconforming and encourage them to complete tasks in their own way. Encourage them to take risks, challenge ideas and to reflect on tasks. If a child learns hundreds of facts but hasn't developed the ability to explore possibilities, much of the knowledge they gain will be wasted.

Thinking 'domains'

Thinking skills can be divided into different areas, or thinking 'domains'. Children need experience of a variety of domains, because each domain has separate aims and develops particular skills. This book offers practice in the following key domains:

- **Critical thinking** encourages children to examine, clarify and evaluate an idea, belief or action. Pupils learn to infer, generalise, take a point of view, hypothesise and find temporary solutions.
- **Decision-making and problem-solving** involve processes such as brainstorming, linking ideas, using analogies, creating original ideas, organising information and looking at a problem from different perspectives. These techniques will enable children to find a variety of solutions to a problem.
- The ability to **collect, retain, recall and use information** when needed is another vital skill.
- **Creative thinking** encourages children to come up with original ideas.

Thinking processes

The activities in this book cover eight processes that are important in promoting thinking skills. These processes can be grouped into cognitive (thinking) and affective (feeling) abilities.

Cognitive abilities
- **Fluency** - thinking of as many ideas as possible
- **Flexibility** - looking at problems from different perspectives; thinking of ways to combine ideas into a new and different solution; grouping objects according to different criteria
- **Originality** - producing unusual or unique ideas
- **Elaboration** - adding or further developing ideas

Affective abilities
- **Curiosity** - working out an idea by instinctively following a certain route
- **Complexity** - thinking of more complex ways of approaching a task, by searching for links, looking for missing sections or restructuring ideas
- **Risk-taking** - making guesses; defending ideas without fear of what others may think
- **Imagining** - picturing and describing something that has never occurred; imagining oneself in other times and places

ASSESSMENT

Allow time for the children to complete activities and give them opportunities to share their ideas in a group. One way in which pupils learn is by mirroring the behaviour and responses of others.
The following are general guidelines for assessing work:
- Display good pieces of work rather than grading them
- Avoid criticising pupils' responses or drawings
- Find something to value whenever possible

Try to achieve continuity in the way pupils are assessed, so that information on each child is cumulative and accurate. A progressive file for each child can include details of their strengths, weaknesses and any special achievements. Note carefully any changes, progress or unusual results, especially in highly creative areas such as story-writing, art, special projects, research, inventions or music. Encourage pupils to examine and assess their own abilities and goals, to gain insight into themselves and the way they tackle problems. You could award fun certificates for proficiency in thinking skills (see page 44).

CLASSROOM ORGANISATION

The classroom environment

The classroom environment can be arranged to allow children to express themselves creatively in tasks. It is helpful to organise materials systematically so that pupils have easy access to them. Use open shelving, plastic boxes and cartons for storing activities and resources. Flexible working and seating areas offer children freedom to move around to different areas of the classroom according to the tasks they are completing. If possible, provide separate areas for independent work, small group work and for the whole class to meet. Try changing the shape of these areas to create interest. You could encourage the children to solve problems using shapes such as hexagons, pentagons, spheres and domes in activities that involve making patterns or building towers.

Colours can be used to set the mood for the type of work pupils will be doing in a particular area of the classroom. Red stimulates thought and orange has an energising effect, while yellow should vitalise the children and speed up mental activity. Green and blue are soothing colours that may calm over-excited children. These colours are ideal to incorporate in a quiet reading area.

Thinking skills learning centres

A thinking skills learning centre could be set up in part of the classroom or as a shared resource for the whole school, perhaps in part of the school library. The learning centre might contain games, puzzles, relevant books and a computer with programs for developing thinking skills. It is a good idea to set up folders of blank worksheets and add new ones regularly. Building materials such as Lego® could be available for constructing unusual objects and devices. You could also provide a book in which pupils can record discoveries or useful tips for pupils working there in future.

Ways to enhance the learning environment

Improve the classroom layout and use displays as visual stimuli.

- Select teaching methods and organisational strategies appropriate to the pupils' needs
- Create a learning environment of high challenge and low stress
- Establish a positive, welcoming atmosphere
- Vary the way pupils work – for example, independently or in small groups
- Aim for a balance between structured and unstructured tasks
- Use a variety of learning styles – for example, hands on, visual, oral, written
- Establish the 'big picture' by linking tasks with pupils' experiences
- Use music to enhance the learning environment and to improve the children's ability to recall information

ICT TIPS

Pupils can be motivated by computer games that allow them to show commitment to a task. Simulation or strategy software encourages children to approach tasks open-mindedly and involves players in critical thinking, risk-taking and real life problem-solving.

ICT skills can be integrated into many aspects of learning. ICT is useful for developing problem-solving skills and the associated thinking skills through the use of existing educational software. Spread sheets and databases can help children to learn more advanced skills, while developing lateral thinking and spatial orientation.

Computer versions of board games can also be used to develop thinking skills. Games such as chess and Scrabble® require children to learn rules and use a variety of strategies.

PARENT INVOLVEMENT

It is beneficial to inform parents that their children are learning thinking skills, as well as encouraging them to support their children's learning at home. Explain that thinking skills enable children to deal with complex situations using a range of thinking strategies, and will equip them to continue learning throughout their lives. On a practical level, parents' help can be enlisted in gathering unusual games and puzzles for a thinking skills learning centre (see page 8).

Parents can help their children to develop thinking skills in many ways, for example: providing opportunities to solve problems creatively; involving the children in planning family outings that take into consideration the needs of all family members; and allowing children to participate in family projects such as redesigning rooms. Most importantly, parents can encourage children to be individuals simply by listening to their ideas. Even if the ideas are unusual or impractical, parents can reassure children that their input is valuable. Children will benefit from being part of a family environment where it is acceptable to make mistakes, and where the emphasis is on learning from those mistakes.

QUICK STARTS

Fairy tales in colour

Read a number of fairy tales to the class, focusing on the use of different colours to create moods, characters and images. Each colour and its purpose should be listed and discussed. Ask the children to suggest other fairy tales where the use of colours is important and discuss the reasons for this.

Population explosion!

Tell the class that they should imagine that the world has become so crowded that people are struggling to find a place to live. The children should list all the ways that the problem could be overcome.

Six words

Present six words to the class and ask pupils to write as many sentences as they can using these words. Can they write a sentence that includes all the words?

Brainstorm!

Have groups of children brainstorm these topics:
• Explain the emotions of a gate.
• Describe the different ways that warmth can be seen.
No answers are right or wrong and the aim is quantity not quality. Have groups share their answers with the class so students can learn from each other's thinking.

Lunch box

Arrange children into small groups and ask them to think of different ways to finish the following sentence: 'This country is like a lunch box because ...'. After they have completed this task, have groups read their answers out and discuss them as a class.

No holidays!

Tell the children to imagine that school holidays, which were due to begin tomorrow, have been cancelled. Pupils should invent and list 20 reasons why this may have happened. Pupils should then tick the three reasons they think are the most creative and share them with the class.

Train delay

Children should imagine that their train has been stopped for an unknown reason and that there will be a long delay. There are 12 other passengers in the carriage. Have pupils invent as many ways as possible to entertain themselves and the other passengers.

Umbrelon

Choose two unrelated objects, such as a melon and an umbrella, and ask pupils to combine them, choose a name for the new object and then list what the qualities of the object are and what the object could be used for. Children could draw the new object and drawings could be displayed around the classroom.

Down the drain

Suggest to pupils that a new netball has fallen into a drain. Have students discuss and list ways of retrieving the netball. Give pupils the following rules: they must not climb in the drain and the only objects available to use are a glove, a wheel and one other item of their choice.

Square eggs!

Ask the children to visualise a square egg. Ask them to explain, in detail, how they think this egg could be used, and what might be the advantages and disadvantages of its shape.

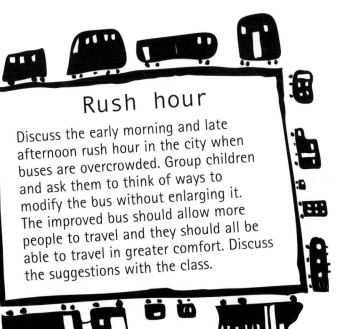

Rush hour

Discuss the early morning and late afternoon rush hour in the city when buses are overcrowded. Group children and ask them to think of ways to modify the bus without enlarging it. The improved bus should allow more people to travel and they should all be able to travel in greater comfort. Discuss the suggestions with the class.

Mouse house

Have pupils design a house for a mouse using lollipop sticks, elastic bands and a serviette. Pupils should draw their design and explain how it works. Designs can be displayed in the classroom.

Be safe!

Have pupils list their ideas on how roads could be made safer for bicycles. They could discuss experiences they have had while riding bicycles where they did not feel safe, and ways these experiences could be avoided.

SCAMPER

SCAMPER is a tool that children can use to redesign an object.
S   Can anything be *substituted*?
C   Can ideas, events or contents be *combined*?
A   Can anything be *adapted*?
M   Can anything be *modified*, magnified or minimised?
P   Can the *purpose* be changed?
E   Can anything be *eliminated*?
R   *Reverse* the pace, order of events and manner.
Ask the children to apply this strategy to redesigning a telephone.

BAR

B makes an object bigger or smaller
A adds on to an object
R replaces, changes or rearranges an object

BAR is useful for helping pupils focus on different facets of an object's design, and can assist them when reversing and redesigning objects for uses other than those for which they were originally intended. Ask pupils to use BAR to redesign a bicycle.

Which article?

Select two newspaper articles giving accounts of the same event. Group pupils and have them study the articles, then discuss how the events are interpreted in each article. Are the events treated in a similar manner? If not, why do they think this might be so?

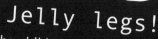

Jelly legs!

Ask the children to imagine that their body is made of jelly. They should then list everyday things that they would not be able to do, and how their jelly body would affect their daily activities. What would they be able to do that they can't do with their current body?

Who's in the zoo?

Have pupils list all the animals they have seen at the zoo. Then have them compare the advantages and disadvantages for animals of living in a zoo. Set aside time for the children to ask any questions they may have about the animals (for example, how the animals are fed and exercised).

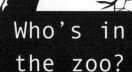

Books, books, books!

Have pupils list and classify the books that the class has read this year. To classify books, pupils can use important characteristics or attributes of characters, objects, places or ideas. Discuss and compare the lists as a class.

Spellcheck!

Ask the children to make a list of the words that they misspell most frequently. Have them classify these words according to what might be possible reasons for misspelling them. Display charts with the correct spellings around the classroom.

ACTIVITY BANK

Great ideas!

List all the ways you can celebrate a holiday.

_____

_____

_____

_____

_____

_____

Suggest different ways that children can amuse themselves when they feel bored.

_____

_____

_____

_____

_____

How many different reasons can you think of why you might not be able to close the front door?

_____

_____

_____

_____

_____

_____

Thinking skill: Fluency

What can you combine?

List all the attributes of a jelly bean. Focus on and think about the feel, the taste, the colour and any other attributes you can think of.

_____

_____

_____

_____

Think about something on the end of a rope and list all its properties.

_____

_____

_____

Link some of the attributes found in the two objects to create something new. Draw this newly-created object and explain how it functions.

_____

_____

_____

_____

Thinking skill: Fluency and flexibility

That's criminal!

Is this a crime?

Work in a group of three. List all the crimes you can think of, for example, harming someone's property, theft, hurting a person, etc.

Rank the crimes from least serious to most serious and write at least three reasons for your answer.

List of crimes	Ranking	Reasons

Thinking skill: Fluency and flexibility

Make a list

The sports day has been postponed for four weeks. Brainstorm all possible reasons.

_____

_____

_____

_____

_____

_____

_____

_____

List as many uses as you can for a bucket.

_____

_____

_____

_____

_____

_____

List all the different ways that you can think of to greet people.

_____

_____

_____

_____

_____

_____

_____

List at least 10 changes that could occur if there were no television programmes being transmitted.

_____

_____

_____

_____

_____

_____

_____

_____

_____

_____

Thinking skill: Fluency and flexibility

Listing change

Write a list of things that change rapidly and a second list of things that change slowly.

Rapid change	**Slow change**

Write a list of things that change daily, for example, world population.	List things that never change.

Thinking skill: Fluency and flexibility

Using technology

Name all the machines that you could possibly use during an average day.

_____   _____

_____   _____

_____   _____

_____   _____

_____   _____

_____   _____

Imagine you were living in the 19th century and were suddenly transported to the present day. What do you imagine you would find most surprising?

_____

_____

_____

_____

_____

_____

_____

What do you think would be most frightening?

_____

_____

_____

What would be most amusing?

_____

_____

What could be most useful out of all the inventions in the 20th century?

_____

_____

Thinking skill: Fluency and flexibility

A question of fame

The answer is "fame".
List five questions.

1. _____
2. _____
3. _____
4. _____
5. _____

Choose a famous person. _____

If you could talk to them, what three questions would you ask them, and what do you think their answers might be?

_____
_____
_____
_____
_____
_____
_____
_____
_____
_____
_____
_____
_____
_____
_____
_____

Thinking skill: Questioning

Asking questions

There was a fire last night and one family's house burnt down. Everyone got out safely but the family has no access to money for a week and no food or shelter.

Brainstorm questions that you would like to ask the family about the scene and their current situation. Place an asterisk (*) next to the three questions that you believe are the most important.

_____

_____

_____

_____

_____

_____

_____

_____

_____

A person who has gone to see a film runs out of the cinema screaming. Brainstorm questions that you would ask bystanders to find possible reasons for this.

_____

_____

_____

_____

_____

_____

_____

_____

Thinking skill: Questioning

What rubbish!

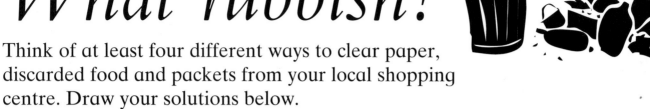

Think of at least four different ways to clear paper, discarded food and packets from your local shopping centre. Draw your solutions below.

Thinking skill: Originality

NAME

What could this be?

List two objects or images that each drawing could be.

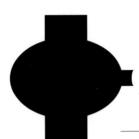

I am an open mouth...

...or a rubber ball.

_____
_____

_____
_____

_____
_____

_____
_____

_____
_____

Draw one of your own and ask a friend to guess what it is.

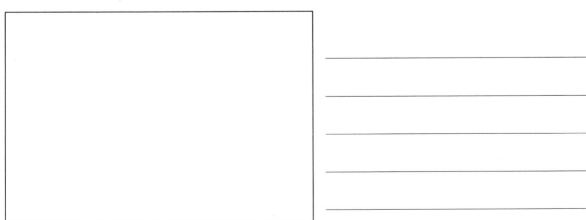

_____
_____
_____
_____

Thinking skill: Forced relationships

Clean the graffiti

Your school has a terrible problem with graffiti. Think of ways that you can stop this happening. Your solution must involve a human, something mechanical and something that has to be eaten.

How will you stop the graffiti writers and sprayers?

_____

_____

_____

_____

_____

_____

Draw your solution here.

Thinking skill: Forced relationships

Picture the scene

Why is the aeroplane's arrival delayed? Think of at least five reasons.

_____

_____

_____

_____

_____

_____

How is a cloud like a pillow? List at least eight attributes or characteristics that are similar.

_____

_____

_____

_____

_____

_____

_____

Imagine that all the clocks have stopped. How would this affect you?

_____

_____

_____

_____

_____

_____

Thinking skill: Imaginative visualisation

Come and play

Imagine you are in a junkyard. There are old tyres, ladders with missing rungs, empty paint tins, boxes, ropes, old cupboards, etc.

Think about how you might use these items to design a safe playground for a number of children. Think about what other recycled items you would like to add for further activities. Write your ideas here.

_____

_____

_____

_____

_____

_____

Draw a map of your new playground in the space below and label its different parts.

Thinking skills: Imaginative visualisation

Land with no gravity

Work in a group of three. Focus on an imaginary land where there is no gravity. Picture the people. What are the colours, shapes, sounds and smells like? Imagine homes, landscape, buildings, traffic, etc.

What are the people doing? Where are they going?

Have one group member draw while the other two describe the scene with their eyes shut. The person drawing can add details as long as these fit with the image. It is a good idea to do a rough drawing before completing a final copy here to ensure that you include all the details.

Thinking skill: Imaginative visualisation

Be creative

Design a device that will save time by doing something that is normally done manually (by hand). Explain how it will work.

Drawing of device

Detailed explanation of how the device will work

_____

_____

_____

_____

_____

_____

_____

Thinking skill: Creative thinking

Brushing plus...

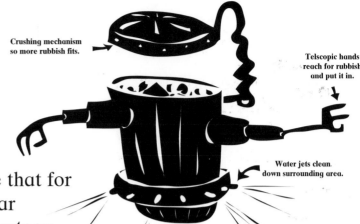

Crushing mechanism so more rubbish fits.

Telscopic hands reach for rubbish and put it in.

Water jets clean. down surrounding area.

Create an improved toothbrush. Ensure that for each change that is made, there is a clear explanation. You could use the BAR strategy to help you consider how different features could be improved.

B = make **bigger** or **smaller**

A = **add** something

R = **remove** something and **replace** it with something else

Thinking skill: Creative thinking

Redesigning a tricycle

Choose five unconnected words.
Check their meanings in a dictionary.

Word   Dictionary meaning

1. _____   _____

2. _____   _____

3. _____   _____

4. _____   _____

5. _____   _____

Now, draw and explain how you would use the five words to make changes to the tricycle. (For example, if you chose the word 'elastic', you might want to design an elastic tricycle that shrinks so it's easy to step on to, then recovers its normal size so you can ride it easily.)

Thinking skill: Creative thinking

New products

Brainstorm ideas for each list.

Different types of clothing,
for example, shoes

_____

_____

_____

_____

_____

_____

Different modes of transport,
for example, train

_____

_____

_____

_____

_____

_____

With your eyes closed, select one object from each list. Combine them to form a new object. Sketch and name the combined idea.

How would this new product affect your life? Describe what it could do.

_____

_____

_____

_____

_____

_____

_____

_____

_____

Thinking skill: Creative thinking

The amazing hat!

Design a hat that has four uses. Draw it here and label all its parts.

Describe how it works and for whom it would be useful.

_____

_____

_____

_____

_____

_____

_____

_____

Thinking skill: Creative thinking

New, improved...

Design a new shower, and explain the reasons for any changes. You may like to use the BAR strategy to help decide on features that could be improved and ways of improving them. Illustrate your new shower design below.

B = make **bigger** or **smaller**

A = **add** something

R = **remove** something and **replace** it with something else

Change: _____

Reasons:_____

_____

Change: _____

Reasons:_____

_____

Change: _____

Reasons:_____

_____

Before...   ## After!

Thinking skill: Creative thinking

List the attributes

Think of at least five attributes that a swing and vacuum cleaner have that are similar.

_____

_____

_____

_____

_____

_____

List and then combine some of the attributes of a child and water to create something new. Draw and describe it below.

Attributes of a child	Attributes of water

New object	Description

Thinking skill: Critical thinking

What a legend!

Describe a hero or heroine who is living at the present time. This can be a fictional or factual person. Start with a physical description and then move beyond this to explain the other qualities they have. Think of 12 heroic tasks that she or he must complete.

Description of hero or heroine	Explain the twelve heroic tasks
	1. _____
	2. _____
	3. _____
	4. _____
	5. _____
	6. _____
	7. _____
	8. _____
	9. _____
	10. _____
	11. _____
	12. _____

You, as the hero, have to select three of the following objects to help with the tasks. Which would you choose and why would they be selected?

Choice	Reasons
_____	_____
_____	_____
_____	_____

matches, jelly beans, pack of cards, rope, skateboard, magnifying glass, newspaper, hat, blanket, boat, bicycle, hammer, nails, money, shoes, soap, spoon, mirror,

Thinking skill: Critical thinking

Look after your feet!

List some attributes of walking boots. Design a new type of boot that includes the most important features or attributes. Add additional protective features to help cope with possible hazards. Include reasons for all changes. You may wish to use the SCUMPS strategy to help determine the attributes.

S = size
C = colour
U = use
M = materials made of
P = parts made up of
S = shape

Attributes of walking boots

_____

_____

_____

_____

Your new design

Thinking skill: Categorising

Out in space...

Work in a group of three. List as many objects as you can think of that you would find in outer space. Think of ways to group or categorise the objects, and give each category or group a label.

List

_____

_____

_____

_____

_____

_____

_____

_____

Items listed under their categories

_____

_____

_____

_____

_____

_____

_____

_____

_____

_____

_____

_____

Thinking skill: Categorising

Look for a pattern

bind, fasten, tighten – words to secure things

swim, jump, run, jog – different ways of moving

Work in a group of two or three. List 30 words from newspaper articles, magazines, a book, etc. They should be varied and not follow one topic.

Word list	Divide the words into groups and describe each group.

Thinking skill: Categorising

Reversing

?taht wonk uoy diD

It has been recorded that Leonardo da Vinci wrote his notes and observations backwards. Why do you think he did this?

_____

_____

_____

How do you think he was able to refer to them?

_____

_____

_____

Think about activities in your daily life. What would you like to reverse? How would you benefit?

Reverse	Benefit

Have someone tell you a message, then write it down backwards.

_____

_____

_____

Can you read back what you have written? How did writing backwards make you feel?

_____

_____

_____

Thinking skill: Interpreting and inferring

Looking at all sides

An animal walking across a busy road has been hit by a passing car. Should you help the animal?

Positives	Negatives	Questions you might have
_____	_____	_____
_____	_____	_____
_____	_____	_____
_____	_____	_____
_____	_____	_____

Summarise by explaining the consequences, potential dangers and problems.

_____

_____

You dislike most of the food in your lunch box every day. Should you empty your lunch box into the waste bin at school each day?

Positives	Negatives	Questions you might have
_____	_____	_____
_____	_____	_____
_____	_____	_____
_____	_____	_____
_____	_____	_____

What decision have you reached?

_____

_____

Thinking skill: Evaluation

Stamp out poverty

World governments should abandon space travel. All money should be directed to help eliminate poverty throughout the world because one-quarter of the world's population is badly malnourished.

Examine the statement. List the positive and negative arguments and any questions that arise.

Positives	Negatives	Questions

What decision did you reach? Do you support the statement?

_____

_____

_____

Thinking skill: Evaluation

Thinking Skills Awards

Awarded to

_____

Fearlessly flexible!

Signed

_____

Date

_____

Awarded to

_____

Intrepid
interpreting!

Signed _____

Date _____

Awarded to

_____

**Thinking skills
wiz!**

Signed _____

Date _____

Awarded to

_____

for original thinking!

Signed _____

Date _____

CHALLENGES

Examining an issue

What you need:

- a newspaper
- pens
- paper

What to do:

1. Work in a group of three.
2. Find an article about a controversial topic. In your group decide on a statement that summarises one side of the controversy (for example, 'Children should not be allowed to take mobile phones to school').
3. Have one group member read the article aloud while the rest of you take notes under the three headings 'Positives', 'Negatives' and 'Questions that arise'.
4. Discuss the notes. Did each note taker see the same positives and negatives?
5. Discuss the issue, referring to your notes. Did your group come to an agreement on the issue, or agree to disagree?
6. Now choose another issue relevant to school (for example, 'Students should be free to choose what they wear to school') and use the same procedure to evaluate and discuss it.

An unusual animal

What you need:

- paper to draw on
- pencil
- eraser
- ruler

What to do:

1. Create an animal and make up a name for it.
2. Describe its appearance, habitat, the food it eats, its enemies, how it keeps itself happy and entertained, and any special features. Draw its footprints. Construct or draw its body and natural habitat.

3. This animal is threatened with extinction. Develop a campaign that will publicise the threat and help save your animal.
4. Your animal is being transported to a zoo. Design a perfect enclosure. Think about its natural environment and what its needs are.

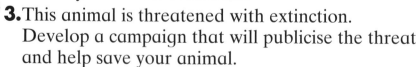

News item

What you need:

- paper to draw on
- pencil
- eraser
- ruler

What to do:

1. Visualise the following scene: engine-driven vehicles have been banned as the pollution is affecting the entire community. The only acceptable means of transport are skateboards and bicycles.

2. Brainstorm the ways the change in transport would affect traffic control, clothing manufacturers, petrol sales, supermarkets and medical care.

3. Develop new road rules for your community. List them so they can be circulated to road users. Ensure that all rules are clarified by appropriate drawings.

Football league

What you need:

- paper
- pencil
- ruler

What to do:

Six schools are taking part in a football tournament at your school. Three pitches are available. Each school plays every other school once and all three pitches must be in use for each round of matches.

1. Work in a group of three or four.

2. Think of names for the six schools.

3. Devise a simple formula to ensure that all schools play each other once.

4. Work out the total number of matches. With three pitches, how many rounds of matches will be needed?

5. Plan the programme of play.

6. Play the matches using dice for scoring.

Skills: Interpreting, evaluating, creative thinking

TASK CARD 5 Enjoy your lunch

What you need:

- a shoebox
- odds and ends
- paper
- pen

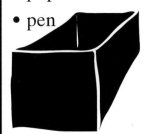

What to do:

1. You want to determine the positives and negatives of the design of a standard lunch box. Develop a questionnaire to survey pupils.

2. Conduct the survey.

3. Prepare a summary of the findings and decide which aspects can be incorporated into a new design for the lunch box. It is important not to lose the positive aspects in your redesign!

4. Draw your new design, explaining the reason for each change.

5. Use a shoebox to construct a protype of your new design.

Skills: Fluency, originality, creative thinking

TASK CARD 6 A new sport

What you need:

- paper to draw on
- pencil
- eraser
- ruler
- cardboard
- scissors

What to do:

1. List all the attributes you can think of for tennis, music and football.

2. Design a new sport for children your age, using a combination of the attributes of each.

3. Develop a set of rules, and design an area for the game to be played on or in. (It might be a court with markings ... or perhaps it would be better suited to an orchestra pit.)

4. Design an advertising campaign to popularise your new sport. What will be its selling points — that it's completely stupid and good fun, or a challenging game that improves fitness and co-ordination ... ?